ABOUT PHONICS

There are just over 40 sounds which go together to make up every single spoken word in the English language. These are called phonemes. Written words are made up of letters which represent these phonemes. In the simplest terms, phonics is linking letters - or combinations of letters - to their phonemes, or phonemes to letters.

Sometimes phonemes are single letter sounds, as in the word 'Ron' which breaks down into three: 'R-o-n'. Sometimes they are not. The word 'thing', for example, is five letters but also breaks down into three phonemes: 'th-i-ng'.

Words can be divided into two basic groups: regular phonic (words such as 'Ron') and irregular (such as 'what'). Regular words, which are far more common, can be sounded out. Irregular words have to be learned.

There are both regular and irregular words in *Goose on the loose*. These have been carefully chosen, and particular phonemes regularly repeated (for example: s-t-ay, p-l-ay, w-ay), so that your child will become familiar with identifying the letter combinations and sounds, and will grow in confidence. On the inside back cover, you'll find a list of words used in the text, broken down into their phonemes and grouped together with words containing similar phonemes.

Read this story with your child, encouraging your child to sound out the words as you go. Soon, most children will start to sound out the words for themselves. This is an excellent way of helping to develop an important reading skill.

Dr. Marlynne Grant

Usborne
Phonics Readers
Goose on the loose

Phil Roxbee Cox

Illustrated by Stephen Cartwright

Edited by Jenny Tyler

Language consultant: Marlynne Grant
BSc, CertEd, MEdPstch, PhD, AFBPs, CPsychol

There is a little yellow duck to find on every page.

First published in 2006 by Usborne Publishing Ltd., Usborne House, 83-85 Saffron Hill, London EC1N 8RT, England. www.usborne.com
Copyright © 2006, 2001 Usborne Publishing Ltd.

Goose is on a scooter.
She can't stay and play.

She's a goose on the loose.
"Get out of my way!"

HONK!

She almost runs down Rooster Ron.

"Get out of my way!"
Goose goes scooting on.

HONK!
HONK!

5

Goose is scooting to Ted's shed...

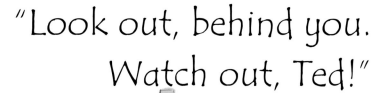

"Look out, behind you.
Watch out, Ted!"

Goose goes scooting down the road.

She almost scoots
right into Toad.

The cows all moo.

The doves all coo.

10

Look out! Goose is on the loose.

She upsets a bunch of kangaroos...

...and shocks a flock of cockatoos.

There are shouts of "hiss!"
and shouts of "boo!"

Then snarls and howls
and a hullabaloo.

"Goose must be stopped! What shall we do?"

But Goose has stopped, and feels a fool.

She's landed in the penguin pool!

ABOUT THE WORDS IN THIS BOOK

Most words in Goose on the loose can be broken down into single letters representing single phonemes (such as 'd-r-o-p-s' and 'e-n-d-s'). There are some words in this book, however, where a combination of letters creates a single phoneme, and these are listed below.

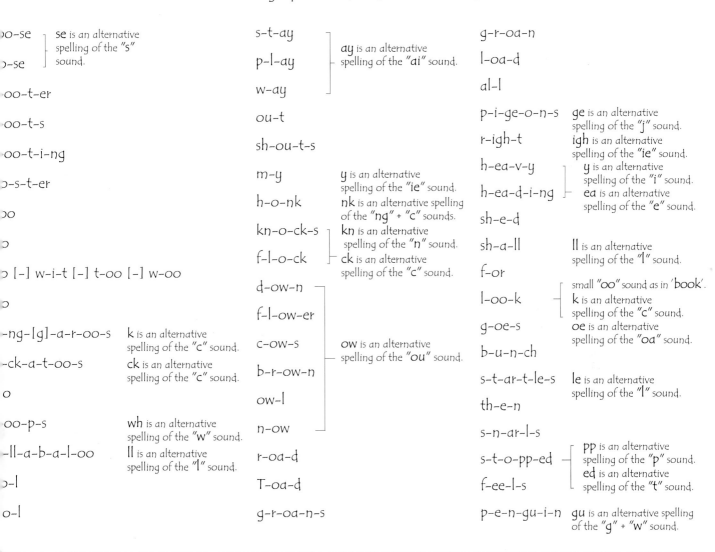

o-se ⎤
       se is an alternative spelling of the "s" sound.
o-se ⎦

oo-t-er

oo-t-s

oo-t-i-ng

o-s-t-er

oo

o

o [-] w-i-t [-] t-oo [-] w-oo

o

-ng-[g]-a-r-oo-s   **k** is an alternative spelling of the "c" sound.

-ck-a-t-oo-s   **ck** is an alternative spelling of the "c" sound.

o

oo-p-s   **wh** is an alternative spelling of the "w" sound.

-ll-a-b-a-l-oo   **ll** is an alternative spelling of the "l" sound.

o-l

o-l

---

s-t-ay ⎤
p-l-ay ⎦   **ay** is an alternative spelling of the "ai" sound.
w-ay ⎦

ou-t

sh-ou-t-s

m-y   **y** is an alternative spelling of the "ie" sound.

h-o-nk   **nk** is an alternative spelling of the "ng" + "c" sounds.

kn-o-ck-s ⎤   **kn** is an alternative spelling of the "n" sound.
f-l-o-ck ⎦   **ck** is an alternative spelling of the "c" sound.

d-ow-n ⎤
f-l-ow-er ⎦
c-ow-s   **ow** is an alternative spelling of the "ou" sound.
b-r-ow-n ⎦
ow-l ⎦
n-ow ⎦

r-oa-d

T-oa-d

g-r-oa-n-s

---

g-r-oa-n

l-oa-d

al-l

p-i-ge-o-n-s   **ge** is an alternative spelling of the "j" sound.

r-igh-t   **igh** is an alternative spelling of the "ie" sound.

h-ea-v-y ⎤   **y** is an alternative spelling of the "i" sound.
h-ea-d-i-ng ⎦   **ea** is an alternative spelling of the "e" sound.

sh-e-d

sh-a-ll   **ll** is an alternative spelling of the "l" sound.

f-or

l-oo-k   small "oo" sound as in 'book'. **k** is an alternative spelling of the "c" sound.

g-oe-s   **oe** is an alternative spelling of the "oa" sound.

b-u-n-ch

s-t-ar-t-le-s   **le** is an alternative spelling of the "l" sound.

th-e-n

s-n-ar-l-s

s-t-o-pp-ed   **pp** is an alternative spelling of the "p" sound. **ed** is an alternative spelling of the "t" sound.

f-ee-l-s

p-e-n-gu-i-n   **gu** is an alternative spelling of the "g" + "w" sound.

IRREGULAR WORDS. These are the words that don't follow the phonic rules completely. Usually, the consonants are regular but the vowels represent different phonemes. You'll need to teach your child how to pronounce these words and to recognize the unexpected parts. Here are the irregular words you'll find in this book:

almost   are   be   behind   do   into   of   says   she   she's   the   there   to   watch   we   what   who   you